Angel! Angel!

Cherie Pless Dittmer

Illustrated by Ed Koehler

SAINT LOUIS

Scripture quotations taken from the HOLY BIBLE, NEW INTERNATIONAL VERSION®. NIV®.
Copyright © 1973, 1978, 1984 by International Bible Society. Used by permission of
Zondervan Publishing House. All rights reserved.

Text copyright © 2002 Cherie Pless Dittmer

Illustrations copyright © 2002 Concordia Publishing House

Published by Concordia Publishing House
3558 S. Jefferson Avenue, St. Louis, MO 63118-3968
Manufactured in China

1 2 3 4 5 6 7 8 9 10   11 10 09 08 07 06 05 04 03 02

To my children Emily, Anna, Erin, Abigail, and Jonathan with whom I love to share Christmas joys and laughter!

This book is also dedicated to all who interact with young children. Read and enjoy this rhythmic telling of our Savior's birth. Allow the children the creative freedom to celebrate this story of God's grace in song, dance, and drama. One reading of this storybook and the children will be eager to say it and sing it and tell it to others. A joyful Christmas sharing will happen!

Angel!
Angel!

What do you see?

I see **Mary**

will have a baby!

Mary! Mary!

What do you see?

I see a **donkey**
carrying me.

Donkey! Donkey!

What do you see?

I see **Joseph** gently leading me.

Joseph! Joseph!

What do you see?

I see an **innkeeper** welcoming me.

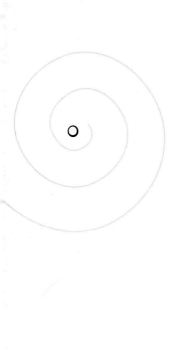

Innkeeper!
InnKeeper!

What do you see?

I see a **spotted cow**
mooing softly.

Spotted Cow!
Spotted Cow!

What do you see?

I see a **wooly sheep**, soft and cuddly.

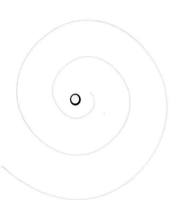

Wooly sheep! Wooly sheep!

What do you see?

I see a **shepherd** carrying me.

Shepherd! Shepherd!

What do you see?

I see the **angels** singing to me.

Angels! Angels!

What do you see?

We see a new **star** shining brightly.

Bright Star!
Bright Star!

What do you see?

I see the **Wise Men** following me.

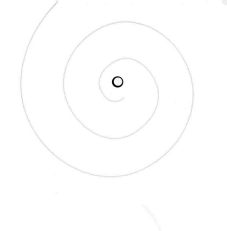

Wise Man! Wise Man!

What do you see?

I see **baby Jesus** smiling at me.

Baby Jesus! Baby Jesus!

What do You see?

I see **God's children** loving Me!

God's Child!
God's Child!

What do **YOU** see?

I see my **Savior,**
who gave His life for me!

For God so loved the world that He gave
His one and only Son, that whoever believes in
Him shall not perish but have eternal life.

John 3:16